CANCER
(23 June-23 July)
Sign — crab
Ruling planet — Moon

LUCKY YOU!
Colour — Lilac
Number — 2
Jewel — Ruby
Day — Saturday

BEST FRIENDS
Taureans, Virgoans, Scorpians and Pisceans are usually chummy with Cancerians.

JUST THE JOB
Nurse, businessman, nursery teacher, sailor, antique dealer, museum assistant or a fisherman.

BAD BITS
(Boo!)
Over-emotional, moody, changeable, untidy and a worrier.

GOOD BITS
(Yippee!)
Maternal, kind, caring, imaginative, romantic, sensitive and patriotic.

SPECIAL DAY IN 1996
April 23

FAMOUS CANCERIANS
Tom Cruise — July 3
Sylvester Stallone — July 6
Tom Hanks — July 9
Corey Feldman — July 16
David Hasselhoff — July 17

BEST FRIENDS
Geminis are chummy with Leos, Librans and Aquarians.

GOOD BITS
(Yippee!)
Clever, lively, talkative, trendy, artistic and fun to be with!

BAD BITS
(Boo!)
Two-faced, cunning, nosy, restless, uptight and a gossip!

FAMOUS GEMINIS
Kylie Minogue — May 28
Prince — June 7
Johnny Depp — June 9
Michael J. Fox — June 9
Steffi Graf — June 14

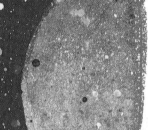

LEO
(24 July-23 August)
Sign — lion
Ruling planet — Sun

GOOD BITS
(Yippee!)
Generous, creative, sunny, broadminded, warm-hearted, and a good organiser.

BAD BITS
(Boo!)
Proud, snobbish, intolerant, power-mad, conceited and a bully!

SPECIAL DAY IN 1996
March 9

FAMOUS LEOS
Sally Gunnell — July 29
Arnold Schwarzenegger — July 30
Whitney Houston — August 9
Madonna — August 16
Belinda Carlisle — August 17

LUCKY YOU!
Colour — Orange
Number — 6
Jewel — Sapphire
Day — Wednesday

JUST THE JOB
Actor, dancer, astrologer, manager, professional sportsman or jeweller.

BEST FRIENDS
Leos are usually friendly with Arians, Geminis, other Leos, Librans and Sagittarians.

VIRGO
(24 August-23 September)
Sign — maiden
Ruling planet — Mercury

JUST THE JOB
Secretary, gardener, accountant, inspector, scientist or anything to do with health and hygiene.

FAMOUS VIRGOANS
Macaulay Culkin — August 26
Lenny Henry — August 29
Gloria Estefan — September 1
Keanu Reeves — September 2
Charlie Sheen — September 3

LUCKY YOU!
Colour — Navy blue
Number — 12
Jewel — Pink jasper
Day — Tuesday

BAD BITS
(Boo!)
Fussy, critical, over-cautious, uptight and usually painfully shy.

GOOD BITS
(Yippee!)
Hard-working, intelligent, careful, down-to-earth, tidy and modest.

BEST FRIENDS
Virgoans are drawn to Taureans, Cancerians, Capricorns and Aquarians.

SPECIAL DAY IN 1996
November 26

Presenting... Bunty

ANNUAL 1996

Aw - can I take him home, please?
See pages 40 and 41.

Printed and Published by D. C. THOMSON & CO., LTD.,
185 Fleet Street, London EC4A 2HS. © D. C. THOMSON & CO., LTD., 1995.
ISBN 0-85116-597-4

8

9

12

Love Letters

HI, I'M ANGIE. GETTING A BOYFRIEND IS EASY! AS EASY AS ABC, IN FACT! JUST READ WHAT HAPPENED TO ME.

A

Angie's all alone —

AWFUL ABSENCE OF ACQUAINTANCES!

B

But beautiful boy's bicycling by . . .

BRILLIANT!

C

COOL!

D

DECIDEDLY DREAMY!

E

ENCHANTING, EVEN!

THE END

Stage Fright

EACH year, one pupil from St Thomas's School was recommended for a scholarship at the famous Marina Academy of Modern Dance and Music.

THIS IS THE TERM WHEN I MAKE MY DECISION ABOUT AWARDING THE MARINA SCHOLARSHIP. AS WELL AS SKILL IN THE PERFORMING ARTS, THE SCHOLARSHIP WINNER MUST SHOW DETERMINATION AND RELIABILITY.

YOU'RE A DEAD CERT FOR IT, WENDY.

However, Terri Preston's best friend, Wendy Gillies, was not popular with everyone.

BET YOU THAT TEACHER'S PET GETS THE SCHOLARSHIP, LEANNE!

YEAH, SHE'S ALWAYS SMARMING ROUND THE STAFF!

IGNORE SUSIE AND LEANNE — THEY'RE JUST JEALOUS. YOU'LL GET THE SCHOLARSHIP BECAUSE YOU'RE THE BEST DANCER AND ACTRESS HERE.

Soon —

TERRI, I WISH YOU WOULDN'T ASSUME I'LL BE AWARDED THE SCHOLARSHIP. YOU'RE AS BAD AS MY MUM AND DAD — THEY CAN'T WAIT TO BOAST ABOUT ME BEING AT THE MARINA ACADEMY!

THAT'S TYPICAL OF WENDY TO BE SO MODEST. YOU ONLY HAVE TO WATCH THE GRACEFUL WAY SHE MOVES TO KNOW SHE'S JUST BORN TO PERFORM ON THE STAGE!

17

B

18

TERRI! AS WENDY WON'T LET ME GO WITH HER, WILL YOU TAKE A PHOTO OF HER IN THE COSTUME?

OKAY, MRS GILLIES.

GO STRAIGHT IN. THE EXTRAS ARE BEING FITTED FOR THEIR COSTUMES ON THE STAGE.

At the theatre —

I DON'T SEE WHY WE NEED CHILDREN IN THE PERFORMANCE!

IT'S GOOD BUSINESS. YOU INVOLVE LOCAL KIDS AND ALL THEIR FRIENDS AND RELATIONS BUY TICKETS TO SEE THEM!

DOESN'T SOUND LIKE WE'RE TOO WELCOME ROUND HERE.

SHE'S ONLY THE WARDROBE MISTRESS, WENDY. LOOK! SHE'S CALLING YOU OVER!

I'D BETTER MAKE SURE THE FLASH IS WORKING, SO I'M READY TO SNAP WENDY IN HER COSTUME.

But just then, the flash went off!

MY COSTUMES!

OH, I CAN'T SEE A THING!

21

WENDY DESERVES THAT SCHOLARSHIP PLACE! I BET SUSIE AND LEANNE ARE BEHIND ALL OF THIS! FROM NOW ON, I'M GOING TO KEEP AN EYE ON THEM.

A few days later, after lessons had finished for the day —

WHERE IS WENDY GILLIES? ISN'T SHE COMING TO READ FOR A PART IN THE NEXT DRAMA PRODUCTION?

MAYBE SHE FEELS SHE'S TOO GOOD FOR SCHOOL PLAYS, SIR!

THAT'S RUBBISH — BUT WHERE *IS* SHE?

WENDY! COME BACK! YOU'RE MISSING YOUR CHANCE TO GET INTO THE NEXT DRAMA PRODUCTION!

OH — ER — BUT SOMEONE TOLD ME THE AUDITIONS HAD BEEN PUT BACK TO NEXT WEEK.

WHO WAS THAT? SUSIE OR LEANNE, I SUPPOSE?

DRAMA Dept.

NO, IT WAS A FIRST-YEAR KID. STILL, THERE'S NO HARM DONE — NOW YOU'VE FOUND ME IN TIME.

Soon —

WHAT'S WENDY PLAYING AT? SHE ISN'T PUTTING ANY EXPRESSION INTO THE PART, YET I KNOW SHE CAN ACT BETTER THAN ANYONE ELSE IN THIS ROOM!

When the cast list was displayed —

CAST LIST

WENDY! YOU DIDN'T GET A PART IN THE PLAY — NOT EVEN AS UNDERSTUDY!

I KNOW I READ BADLY. I — I JUST DON'T FEEL LIKE ACTING AT THE MOMENT.

22

23

WENDY! I...I DON'T BELIEVE IT!

THIS IS THE PHOTO I TOOK BY ACCIDENT AT THE THEATRE — AND IT SHOWS YOU DELIBERATELY PUSHING THE COSTUME RAIL OFF THE STAGE!

SO IT WAS *YOU* ALL THE TIME — *YOU* WERE YOUR OWN ENEMY!

I — I DIDN'T WANT THAT SCHOLARSHIP, BUT MUM AND DAD KEPT PUSHING ME! I'M AFRAID OF GOING TO A NEW SCHOOL. I LIKE IT AT ST THOMAS'S — AND BESIDES — IT WOULD HAVE SPLIT US UP, AND WE'VE BEEN BEST FRIENDS SINCE JUNIOR SCHOOL!

I BET YOU HATE ME NOW!

NO, I DON'T — I'M STILL YOUR BEST FRIEND. AND I'M SURE YOUR MUM AND DAD WILL UNDERSTAND.

Later —

OH, DARLING, WHY DIDN'T YOU TELL US EARLIER? WE ONLY WANT WHAT'S BEST FOR YOU. WE DON'T WANT TO SEE YOU UNHAPPY.

And, at the start of the new term —

MARINA SCHOLARSHIP

WELL, ONE GOOD THING CAME OF IT, WENDY. SUSIE SHARP GOT THE SCHOLARSHIP AND WON'T BE AROUND TO BE NASTY TO US FOR THE NEXT YEAR.

YES, BUT YOU KNOW, TERRI, I'M GOING TO HAVE A REAL TRY FOR THAT SCHOLARSHIP NEXT YEAR. I'M GOING TO MAKE MUM AND DAD PROUD OF ME!

THE END

24

26

27

29

31

MATCHMAKER MARIE

MARIE DUNCAN was worried about her widower dad.

COME ON, UNITED! THAT'S THE STUFF!

DAD SPENDS ALL HIS TIME WORKING, LOOKING AFTER ME, AND WATCHING TV. I CAN'T REMEMBER WHEN HE LAST WENT OUT FOR FUN.

DAD, WHY DON'T YOU GO AND SEE UNITED PLAY FOR REAL, INSTEAD OF WATCHING THEM ON TV? I'LL GO WITH YOU, IF YOU LIKE.

I WOULDN'T DO THAT TO YOU, LOVE. I KNOW HOW MUCH YOU HATE WATCHING FOOTBALL. I'M QUITE HAPPY BEING A COUCH POTATO ON SATURDAY AFTERNOON.

IT'S NOT JUST SATURDAY AFTERNOON, THOUGH. POOR DAD NEVER GOES OUT AT ALL. IT'S FIVE YEARS SINCE MUM DIED. MAYBE IT'S TIME HE FOUND HIMSELF A GIRLFRIEND?

But, a week later —

GOOD NEWS, MARIE! I'VE TAKEN YOUR ADVICE AT LAST! I'M GOING TO GET OUT AND ABOUT A BIT MORE!

NOTHING SO ENERGETIC, LOVE. I'M GOING TO DO A CLASS ON COMPUTING ON MONDAY EVENINGS. IT'LL HELP ME AT WORK.

OH, DAD — THAT'S REALLY BORING!

HEY, DAD — THAT'S BRILLIANT! WHAT ARE YOU GOING TO DO — SQUASH? BADMINTON? OR ARE YOU TAKING UP DISCO DANCING?

HE'S HARDLY LIKELY TO MEET ANY NICE LADIES AT A COMPUTING CLASS.

33

AARGH! MY ANKLE!

But —

ARE YOU ALL RIGHT, MARIE?

DAD AND MISS CURTISS ARE BOUND TO MEET NOW.

NO NEED FOR YOU TO STOP, SALLY, YOU'LL MISS YOUR TRAIN. I'VE GOT A FIRST AID CERTIFICATE, AFTER ALL.

ARE YOU HURT, LOVE?

NO, DAD.

EXCEPT FOR MY PRIDE! I'VE BLOWN IT AGAIN. THERE'S NO WAY THAT DAD'S GOING TO GET ROMANTIC WITH MRS MILLER. SHE'S MARRIED WITH THREE KIDS AND MISS CURTISS HAS GONE.

Next day —

ARE YOU ALL RIGHT AFTER YOUR FALL YESTERDAY, MARIE?

YES, FINE, THANKS.

IF I DON'T THINK OF SOMETHING FAST, MISS CURTISS WILL BE SNAPPED UP BY SOMEONE ELSE BEFORE SHE EVEN MEETS MY DAD.

Luckily, Marie soon had another chance to get her two favourite people to meet up!

PARENTS' EVENING ON TUESDAY, EH? I'LL CERTAINLY BE ALONG FOR THAT. I LIKE TO KEEP UP WITH HOW YOU'RE DOING IN SCHOOL, LOVE.

THAT'S NICE, DAD. WE'VE GOT A FEW NEW TEACHERS ON THE STAFF THIS YEAR.

AND ONE IN PARTICULAR THAT I'M DYING FOR YOU TO MEET.

Later —

I'M OFF TO MY COMPUTER CLASS NOW, LOVE. YOU'LL BE OKAY WITH GRAN UNTIL I GET BACK, WON'T YOU?

YOU LOOK REALLY COOL, DAD. IS THAT A NEW SUIT?

MAYBE THE COMPUTING CLASS WASN'T SUCH A BAD IDEA AFTER ALL? DAD HAS CERTAINLY SMARTENED HIMSELF UP SINCE HE STARTED GOING OUT A BIT MORE.

37

THE END

38

FIONA'S FIRST DAY

FIONA MORRIS felt sick with worry. The night before she had prepared everything for today — the first day of the term as well as her first day at Greenford High School. Her new uniform looked smart. At least she would look the same as all the other girls, even if she didn't know what to do or where to go.

She said goodbye to her mum and younger sister, picked up her school bag, and went out.

The closer she got to the school the worse she felt. There were so many people all going to the school, and yet she seemed to be the only one who was alone.

She thought that no-one would want to be friends with her because they already had friends of their own. How she wished that Dad hadn't been made redundant! Then she would be happily back at the private school, with all her old friends.

She went through the gates and towards the front door of the main school building. It was the way she had come in when she first visited the school to see the Head.

She was about to open the door when she heard a voice saying, "Look at her! Just because she's got a smart new uniform she thinks she owns the place! Fancy not knowing that only teachers use the front door!"

Fiona turned round and saw a group of girls watching her. She knew her face was going very red. What should she do? She couldn't go through the door now, but neither did she feel brave enough to walk past those girls.

Just then, the school secretary appeared. Instantly, she seemed to understand the situation and went up to Fiona and said, "Come in this way to the office. Although we don't like everyone using this door, it is the quickest way, especially when you don't know your way around!"

Fiona followed her with a feeling of relief. She wondered if she would meet that group of girls again, hoping very much that she wouldn't!

After seeing the Head, she was taken to Miss Sanderson, her form teacher, who introduced her to the class. As Fiona looked round, she froze — all those girls who had laughed at her were

there! They were grinning away like mad, obviously enjoying her distress.

Fiona tried to listen to what was being said to her, but she wasn't really taking it in. She just wished she could run away — anywhere, as long as it was away from that horrible group of girls.

"Now, sit over there beside Marcia," the teacher told Fiona.

"Don't worry," said Marcia. "I'll see you're okay. It's double Maths first, then History."

Fiona followed Marcia along the winding corridors to the Maths room, where she was introduced to Mr Storman.

"I need to find out what you know, so I want you to do a test for me," he told Fiona.

Fiona was taken into an office where she was given a question sheet.

"Do as much as you can," he said kindly. "Don't bother with the bits you don't know."

With that, he left her alone.

Fiona enjoyed Maths and the questions didn't seem too difficult. Soon she had finished.

Then she started to worry about the 'Grinning Gang'. Did they know she had been at a private school? Would they think she was a snob? Would they bully her?

Just then, Mr Storman returned.

"Oh, good! You've finished. Now, come back in — I'm about to set this week's homework."

Back in the classroom, Fiona didn't know where to sit. She couldn't see Marcia, so she sat down at the nearest empty desk.

Then she saw who she was sitting next to! It was one of the 'Grinning Gang'! She couldn't move now, so she made sure that she concentrated hard on everything that Mr Storman was saying, and tried not to worry about her problem.

"Gosh," said the girl beside her. "I didn't understand a word of that! Do *you* know what to do?"

"Well — er — yes," Fiona replied, taken aback, for this girl was actually *smiling* at her. A friendly smile — not a nasty grin like before.

"I hope we didn't upset you this morning," the girl said. "We do it to every new girl. We know they'll go to the front door and, although it doesn't really matter, we make them think they've done something bad! I'm sorry. It isn't very nice, I suppose, but we don't mean any harm. Come on, meet the others and I'll get them to grovel to you!"

Suddenly, Fiona felt that a great weight had been lifted from her shoulders. She felt happy — they weren't going to be nasty to her after all.

"Don't worry about it," she answered. "But first I must find Marcia. I'll probably see you all later."

Fiona smiled to herself. Maybe her new school wasn't going to be so bad after all.

THE END

Laura's Notepaper

Dear Bunty,
    I have been reading Bunty for about three years. When you print photos of girls who have been somewhere interesting, I wonder how they get to be in Bunty. I would love to be one of them. If you consider this, I would like to help out at Battersea Dogs' Home because I love dogs and would like to see how they care for them.
                Yours hopefully,
                    Laura Croker.

Grub's up!

Aw!

In The

It's a cat's life, too!

Laura in one of the Home's vans which picks up strays.

That's where Bunty reader, Laura

Laura loves dogs and wrote in to ask us if she could visit Battersea Dogs' Home, see how they were looked after, and help out! Well, we (and Battersea Dogs' Home) didn't need to be asked twice! Here's how Laura got on!

A normal day for staff at the Home starts around 8 am, where their first job is to clean out the kennels. Luckily, Laura was spared that, but she quickly got involved in the day's next important job — feeding. The dogs are fed twice a day, on a complete diet — dry biscuits with all the minerals and vitamins dogs need.

Next came exercising and playing, where as many dogs as possible were allowed to run around and play with each other, watched over by the Home's staff.

To work at Battersea Dogs' Home, you don't need set, formal qualifications. A love of animals is far more important — as is dedication to the job. Everything else can be picked

It's a dog's life!

Making a sale.

Dogs' House!

Checking out potential owners.

Laura and Dot.

Croker, ended up when we took her to Battersea Dogs' Home!

up as you go along — although you normally have to be eighteen before you can work there. The hours are long — you have to work weekends and even over Christmas — and it's not well paid. But if, like Laura, you love animals, it's the perfect job!

The dogs are bathed and groomed as often as possible — there's nothing quite like a good brush to keep a dog's coat healthy.

As well as mucking in with the all-important kennel work, Laura also visited the pharmacy where 12 veterinary nurses (including trainees) and a full time vet are on hand to tend to any ill dogs or cats.

Yes, Battersea Dogs' Home cares for cats, too! Another of Laura's jobs was actually accepting payment from a man buying a cat, and helping out in the shop which sells a wide variety of pet products as well as T-shirts and sweatshirts.

Of course the main part of Battersea Dogs' Home work

involves trying to ensure that all the cats and dogs which find themselves there end up in nice, new homes with kind, loving owners.

All potential owners have to complete a thorough questionnaire. Staff at Battersea Dogs' Home go through it with them, ask further questions, do pre-visits to check out an animal's new home, and then follow this up with after-visits to see how the animal's settled in.

At the end of her day, Laura had her picture taken with one of her favourite dogs — Dot, a lovable dog with two different coloured eyes. Laura doesn't have a dog of her own, but is always asking her dad if she can get one!

Had Laura enjoyed her day?

"Very much! It's been great! I've enjoyed doing everything!"

Thanks very much to everyone at Battersea Dogs' Home for all their help.

41

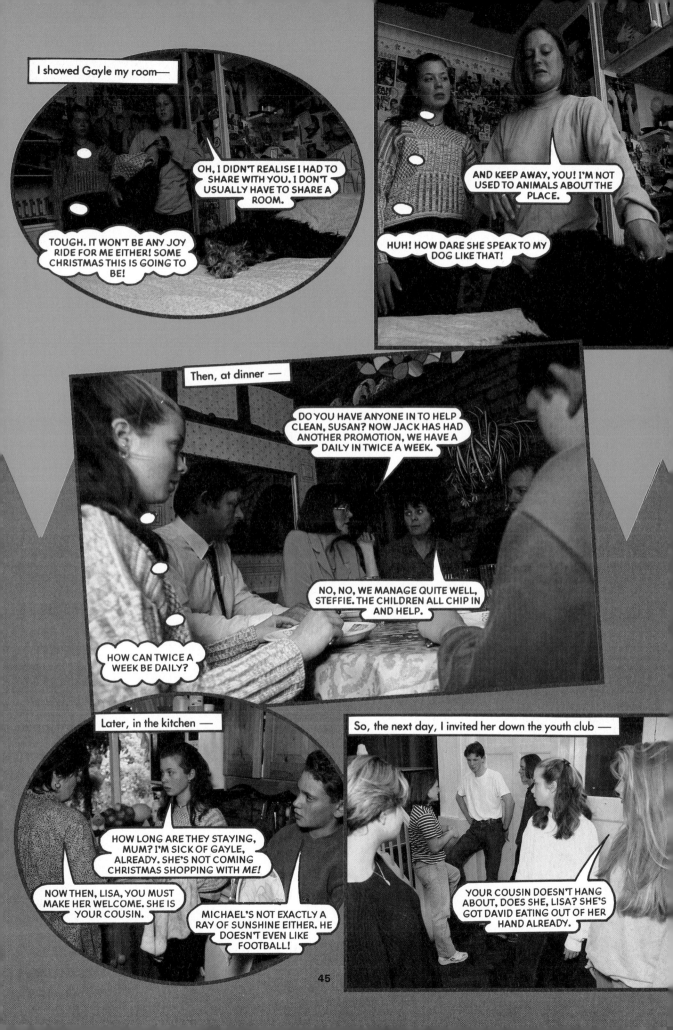

45

46

Then, guess who arrived as Becky and Karen were leaving?

HI! WHERE'S GAYLE? I SAID I'D MEET HER HERE.

SHE'S, UM, NIPPED OUT TO DO SOME SHOPPING. SHE SHOULDN'T BE LONG.

I'LL KILL HER FOR THIS.

He waited, but —

SURE.

LOOKS LIKE SHE'S TAKING LONGER THAN EXPECTED. I'LL HAVE TO GO. WILL YOU TELL HER I CALLED?

I'LL TELL HER ONE OR TWO HOME TRUTHS, TOO.

THEY'RE MY MATES, GAYLE. I'D PREFER IF YOU DIDN'T MESS THEM AROUND.

HUH? I'M ONLY HAVING A LAUGH. THEY'RE BOTH REALLY TOO DAGGY FOR ME. NO WONDER THEY'RE *YOUR* MATES!

AT LEAST I DO HAVE SOME MATES WHICH I GUESS IS MORE THAN A STUCK UP, SELF-CENTRED GIMP LIKE YOU HAS!

EH?

The next day, the garage sale went well—

DAVID AND MARK ARE BOTH IGNORING GAYLE NOW. SOMEONE MUST HAVE SNITCHED ON HER.

No Boys Allowed!

THIRTEEN-YEAR-OLD Sammi Palmer fancied Graham Rogers, so she was thrilled when he asked her out.

WE'LL ARRANGE SOMETHING TOMORROW THEN, SAMMI.

SURE! SEE YOU GRAHAM.

WHAT WAS ALL THAT ABOUT?

GRAHAM'S ASKED ME OUT! ISN'T IT GREAT, HELEN?

But, at home —

GUESS WHAT? GRAHAM ROGERS HAS ASKED ME TO GO OUT WITH HIM!

I'M SORRY, SAMMI — BUT THIRTEEN IS TOO YOUNG TO DATE BOYS.

I AGREE WITH YOUR DAD.

HUH! MUM AND DAD ARE THE PITS! THEY'RE SO OLD-FASHIONED!

I DON'T KNOW WHAT YOU'RE MAKING SUCH A FUSS ABOUT. BOYS ARE SILLY, ANYWAY.

IT'S NOT FAIR! THE NICEST BOY IN SCHOOL ASKS ME OUT AND I CAN'T GO.

UNLESS . . . MAYBE I CAN! I DON'T CARE *WHAT* MUM AND DAD SAY. I *WILL* GO OUT WITH GRAHAM — BEHIND THEIR BACKS!

So, next day —

HAVE YOU SPOKEN TO GRAHAM, THEN?

YES, HE'S TAKING ME TO THE BURGER BAR AFTER SCHOOL TOMORROW!

SO EVERYTHING'S FINE? LUCKY YOU!

WELL . . . NOT QUITE EVERYTHING. MUM AND DAD SAID I COULDN'T GO. THEY THINK I'M TOO YOUNG FOR BOYFRIENDS. BUT I DON'T CARE! I'M GOING OUT WITH GRAHAM BEHIND THEIR BACKS!

51

52

CONTINUED ON PAGE 71

53

LOOKING FOR LIZZIE

ONE day, in Victorian times, a fair came to Westford, where Rebecca Williams lived with her parents and younger sister, Vicky.

IT'S THE FAIR, VICKY! I CAN SEE A CART WITH THE PAINTED HORSES FOR THE ROUNDABOUT. THE FAIR ORGAN'S PLAYING. CAN YOU HEAR THE MUSIC?

YES, I CAN HEAR IT. I WISH I COULD SEE IT ALL, TOO, REBECCA. I'VE NEVER BEEN TO A FAIR. I WOULD SO LOVE TO GO. HERE'S MY LIZZIE! SHE WANTS TO SEE THE FAIR, TOO.

THERE! LIZZIE CAN SEE IT ALL! NOW YOU CAN PRETEND SHE'S GOING TO TELL YOU ALL ABOUT IT.

POOR LITTLE VICKY! SHE'S TOO WEAK EVEN TO COME TO THE WINDOW. IF ONLY SHE WOULD GET BETTER — SHE HAS BEEN ILL FOR SO LONG.

ONE DAY SOON, WHEN YOU ARE BETTER, WE'LL GO TO THE FAIR! YOU'LL RIDE ROUND ON A BEAUTIFUL HORSE ON THE ROUNDABOUT. THAT'S A PROMISE!

OH, REBECCA — I'D LOVE THAT! I *WILL* GET BETTER! ONE DAY I'LL WALK AGAIN AND WE'LL GO TO THE FAIR. I CAN DREAM ABOUT IT!

56

Next day —

I'M SO WORRIED ABOUT VICKY. SHE'S HARDLY EATEN ANYTHING SINCE HER DOLL VANISHED.

OUR POOR LITTLE GIRL! WE MUST CALL THE DOCTOR AGAIN, MARIA.

THERE IS VERY LITTLE I CAN DO FOR THE CHILD, MRS WILLIAMS. A TONIC MAY HELP, BUT I FEAR SHE MAY LOSE THE WILL TO FIGHT.

I CAN'T JUST STAND BY AND WATCH VICKY GROW WEAKER EVERY DAY. THERE MUST BE SOMETHING I CAN DO TO HELP!

That evening —

THE BURGLARS MUST HAVE TAKEN LIZZIE. I'LL GO AFTER THE FAIR AND FIND HER! IT WON'T BE EASY, BUT IF IT'S THE ONLY WAY TO HELP VICKY I'LL HAVE TO TRY IT.

I HATE TO LEAVE VICKI AND MAMA AND PAPA LIKE THIS, BUT AT LEAST I CAN FEEL I'M DOING SOMETHING TO HELP. I'VE PACKED SOME FOOD AND MONEY, AND MY JEWELLERY.

I HEARD PEOPLE SAYING THE FAIR WAS MOVING ON TO HILWORTH. THAT'S TEN MILES AWAY, OVER THE HILL, SO I'LL START MY SEARCH THERE.

57

THANK GOODNESS I CAN SLEEP FOR A LITTLE WHILE. THERE WILL BE MANY MORE MILES TO WALK BEFORE I FIND LIZZIE!

An hour later —

MANY THANKS!

ONLY ONE MILE TO LONG BRADBURY! I CAN BE THERE BEFORE IT IS DARK. THERE'S NO TIME TO STOP, BUT I CAN EAT SOME BREAD AND CHEESE AS I WALK.

OH, NO! ALL MY MONEY'S GONE! THAT BOY MUST HAVE TAKEN IT WHILE I WAS ASLEEP. THEY SEEMED SO FRIENDLY — I THOUGHT I COULD TRUST THEM. BUT MY JEWELLERY'S STILL HERE, THANK GOODNESS.

As Rebecca approached Long Bradbury —

THE FAIR IS HERE! I CAN HEAR THE MUSIC.

WHERE CAN I START LOOKING FOR LIZZIE? I CAN'T SEE HER ON ANY OF THE STALLS. MAYBE SOMEONE CAN REMEMBER SEEING HER?

HAVE I SEEN A RAG DOLL? OF COURSE NOT! NOW GET OUT OF THE WAY, GIRL. I HAVE CUSTOMERS WAITING.

BUT, I — OH!

OH, NO YOU DON'T! THAT'S MY DAUGHTER'S DOLL. I'VE A GOOD MIND TO CALL THE CONSTABLE.

NO! IT'S MY SISTER'S! SOMEONE TOOK IT WHILE THE FAIR WAS IN WESTFORD. MY LITTLE SISTER'S VERY ILL AND LOSING HER DOLL HAS MADE HER WORSE. I CAME TO FIND IT SO SHE WOULD GET BETTER AGAIN. PLEASE LET ME HAVE IT.

SO YOU WANT THE DOLL BACK, DO YOU? WE COULD MAKE A BARGAIN. I'LL LET YOU TAKE THE DOLL BACK IF YOU AGREE TO STAY HERE AND WORK FOR ME. THAT'S FAIR, AIN'T IT?

NO! SHE'S HORRIBLE! I COULDN'T BEAR TO WORK FOR HER. BUT WHAT OF POOR LITTLE VICKY? SHE'S GROWING WEAKER ALL THE TIME. I'LL HAVE TO AGREE!

VERY WELL! BUT FIRST LIZZIE MUST BE TAKEN BACK TO VICKY. AFTER THAT I'LL WORK FOR YOU.

I KNEW YOU'D SEE SENSE, GIRL. WE'LL TRAVEL THERE TONIGHT. THERE ARE SOME OLD CLOTHES IN THE CARAVAN YOU CAN WEAR. THOSE FANCY CLOTHES OF YOURS ARE TOO GOOD FOR A FAIRGROUND SKIVVY.

Late that night —

RIGHT, GET A MOVE ON! YOU CAN LEAVE THE DOLL ON THE DOORSTEP.

NO! I MUST LEAVE HER IN VICKY'S ROOM! DON'T WORRY — I'LL COME BACK TO YOU. I WON'T BREAK MY WORD.

I'M COMING WITH YOU — JUST IN CASE. AND DON'T TRY ANY TRICKS OR IT'LL BE THE WORSE FOR YOUR SISTER.

I'D BETTER DO AS SHE SAYS OR SHE MIGHT HURT VICKY.

THERE! LIZZIE HAS COME BACK TO YOU! NOW YOU CAN GROW STRONG AND WELL AGAIN.

A few minutes later —

OH, MAMA AND PAPA — WILL I EVER SEE YOU AGAIN? I FEEL MY HEART IS BREAKING, HAVING TO LEAVE YOU LIKE THIS. I DREAD TO THINK WHAT THE FUTURE HOLDS FOR ME.

Back at the fairground —

YOU'LL SLEEP WITH THE DOGS. IN THE MORNING YOU CAN LIGHT THE FIRE AND FETCH THE WATER. THE DOGS WILL MAKE SURE YOU DON'T MAKE OFF IN THE NIGHT.

SO THAT'S WHERE MY PLACE WILL BE — WITH THE DOGS! I SUPPOSE I'D BETTER GET USED TO IT.

Next day —

HAVEN'T YOU FINISHED YET, YOU LAZY BRAT? THERE'S A MEAL TO COOK AND THEN THE WASHING TO DO.

I'VE BEEN WORKING SINCE DAYLIGHT WITHOUT EVEN A CRUST TO EAT. THE DOGS ARE TREATED BETTER THAN ME — AT LEAST THEY'VE HAD A BONE TO GNAW.

Later —

THE FAIR'S MOVING ON NORTH TONIGHT. GO AND HELP TO TAKE THE STALLS DOWN.

SO WE'LL BE TRAVELLING NORTH — AWAY FROM WESTFORD AND MAMA AND PAPA AND VICKY. I THOUGHT WE MIGHT HAVE MOVED NEARER, BUT IT'S NO USE HOPING NOW. I'LL NEVER SEE MY HOME AGAIN!

Several weeks passed. Exhausted and unhappy, Rebecca lost count of the days as the fair moved on from one town to another. One morning —

IN THE CARAVAN, BRAT! QUICKLY!

GET IN THERE AND KEEP QUIET!

WHAT'S GOING ON?

debbie's designs

NO WONDER THE ROOF'S LEAKING. THAT WIND LAST NIGHT TOOK OFF ANOTHER LOT OF TILES.

YOU'LL HAVE TO GET THE WORKMEN IN, MUM!

DEBBIE SAUNDERS lived with her older sister Cynthia and their widowed mum.

So —

I GOT AN ESTIMATE OF FIVE HUNDRED POUNDS FOR ROOF REPAIRS. WE CAN'T AFFORD THAT.

DON'T WORRY, MUM! I'LL GO UP IN THE ATTIC AND POP BUCKETS UNDER THE LEAKS.

Later —

WHAT I NEED IS A WAY TO GET EXTRA CASH! MY SHOP ASSISTANT'S WAGE IN SUPASPEND IS PATHETIC, AND AFTER I'VE GIVEN MUM THE MONEY FOR MY KEEP, I CAN'T AFFORD TO BUY ANYTHING NEW TO WEAR.

YOU'VE GOT TO BE JOKING, CYNTHIA. THAT WARDROBE'S FULL OF CLOTHES!

THIS IS THE END! I'VE NOT A DECENT RAG TO MY BACK, AND NOW WE'VE SPRUNG ANOTHER LEAK!

MAYBE I CAN HELP YOU OUT, SIS! I'VE DESIGNED YOU A GREAT NEW OUTFIT.

64

I CALL THIS MY 'RAINY DAY' ENSEMBLE. THE UMBRELLA-CAPE WILL PROTECT YOU FROM THE DRIPS COMING THROUGH THE CEILING, AND THE ELEGANT WELLIE-BOOTS ARE AN OPTIONAL EXTRA.

HEY, THIS ISN'T BAD, DEBBIE. I DIDN'T KNOW YOU COULD MAKE DESIGNS LIKE THIS.

Later —

MAYBE THERE'S A CHANCE TO GET A BIT OF EXTRA MONEY AFTER ALL! GOOD JOB I NOTICED THIS IN THE MAGAZINE!

N.E.W FASHION MONTHLY

Several weeks later —

HEY — I'VE WON FIVE HUNDRED POUNDS! ER — IT WAS A —A SORT OF QUIZ IN MY FASHION MAG! THE CHEQUE WILL BE PRESENTED TO ME NEXT SATURDAY MORNING AT THE GREAT CARLTON HOTEL, IN TOWN.

MAYBE I KNOW MY SISTER TOO WELL, BUT SHE LOOKS A BIT GUILTY TO ME. WHAT'S SHE BEEN UP TO?

I'LL BE WORKING, SO I CAN'T GO WITH YOU, DEAR.

THAT'S OKAY, MUM, I'LL KEEP OUR PRIZEWINNER COMPANY.

OH — YOU DON'T HAVE TO! IT'LL PROBABLY BE REALLY BORING.

But at the prize-giving —

YOU'VE SEEN THE RUNNERS-UP, BUT NOW IS THE TIME TO APPLAUD OUR WINNING FASHION DESIGN.

I THOUGHT YOU SAID YOU ENTERED A QUIZ!

OH, SHUT UP! WHAT DOES IT MATTER HOW I WON THE MONEY?

HERE IT IS — THE 'RAINY DAY' ENSEMBLE WHICH WAS THE WORK OF MISS CYNTHIA SAUNDERS!

THAT'S MY DESIGN, NOT CYNTHIA'S! NO WONDER SHE WASN'T KEEN ON ME COMING!

Later —

OKAY, I BENT THE COMPETITION RULES A BIT! I HAD TO SEND IT IN UNDER MY NAME, BECAUSE ENTRANTS HAD TO BE OVER EIGHTEEN.

MUM WILL MAKE YOU HAND IT BACK. EVEN THOUGH WE'RE HARD UP, SHE WOULDN'T AGREE TO YOUR BEING DISHONEST.

Later, at home —

I'VE GIVEN MY SISTER TEN MINUTES ALONE WITH MUM, TO LET HER EXPLAIN WHAT SHE DID. I HOPE MUM WON'T BE TOO MAD AT HER.

CYNTHIA INSISTS ON GIVING ME HER PRIZE MONEY TO PAY FOR THE ROOF REPAIRS! I HAVE TO ADMIT I'VE BEEN SO WORRIED ABOUT THOSE LEAKS, I'VE NOT BEEN SLEEPING!

IF YOU GO ON LIKE THAT YOU'LL BE ILL, MUM. WE WOULDN'T WANT THAT, WOULD WE, DEBBIE?

YOU PUT ME INTO THE POSITION WHERE I COULDN'T REALLY TELL MUM ABOUT YOU BEING A CHEAT!

I'D HAVE LIKED TO HAVE USED THAT CASH TO BUY NEW CLOTHES — BUT AT LEAST WE'LL BE DRY!

But the following week —

I'VE DONE IT! I'VE HANDED IN MY NOTICE AT THE SHOP. I TOLD THAT OLD BAT OF A MANAGERESS SHE CAN GET SOMEONE ELSE TO RUN AROUND AFTER HER STUPID CUSTOMERS, BECAUSE I'VE GOT A NEW JOB!

SINCE WHEN?

IT ALL CAME FROM THAT COMPETITION! THE 'DEL-DINA' FASHION COMPANY HEARD ABOUT IT. THEY WANT ME TO ADVISE ON THEIR NEW TEENAGE FASHION RANGE.

BY WINNING THAT QUIZ, I SUPPOSE YOU SHOWED A GOOD KNOWLEDGE OF FASHION.

WE BOTH KNOW IT WASN'T ANSWERING A QUIZ THAT GOT YOU INTO THE SPOTLIGHT!

JUST LET ME EXPLAIN. 'DEL-DINA' FASHIONS WANTS ME AS A DESIGNER, BUT I COULDN'T TELL MUM THAT. SHE KNOWS I CAN'T DRAW OR DESIGN ANYTHING!

THEY OFFERED ME FOUR TIMES WHAT I'VE BEEN EARNING. I COULDN'T TURN IT DOWN WHEN I REMEMBERED THIS HUGE PILE OF BILLS WAITING AT HOME. I DON'T WANT THE MONEY FOR MYSELF — IT'S TO MAKE LIFE EASIER FOR MUM.

BUT YOU CAN'T DESIGN CLOTHES.

LISTEN! I'LL BE WORKING FROM HOME, SO YOU COULD DO THE DESIGNS FOR ME. I ADMIT IT'S NOT TOTALLY HONEST, AND I PROMISE TO RESIGN, ONCE WE'VE PAID OFF THE BILLS.

Suddenly, life became much harder for Debbie —

MY BOSS AT 'DEL-DINA' HAS BEEN ON THE PHONE. HE WANTS SOME IDEAS FOR CASUAL JACKETS. CAN YOU KNOCK OFF A FEW SKETCHES BEFORE MUM GETS HOME FROM WORK?

I'M SUPPOSED TO BE REVISING FOR A FRENCH TEST, AS WELL AS DOING MATHS AND HISTORY HOMEWORK.

THESE ARE TERRIFIC! WE MAKE A GOOD TEAM.

ME WORKING AND YOU LOUNGING ABOUT ALL DAY, YOU MEAN?

HOPE YOU'VE NOTHING PLANNED FOR THE WEEKEND, I PROMISED SOME T-SHIRT DESIGNS FOR MONDAY.

I HAD A TRIP TO THE CINEMA WITH SALLY ARRANGED FOR SATURDAY, AND SKATING ON SUNDAY! I CAN'T CANCEL AND LET HER DOWN. I'LL JUST HAVE TO FIT THE DESIGNING IN SOME TIME.

So, in the early hours of Monday morning —

IT'S ALMOST THREE IN THE MORNING! MUM WOULD HAVE A FIT IF SHE FOUND ME WORKING, BUT THESE DESIGNS TOOK LONGER THAN I THOUGHT!

67

WAKEN UP, DEBBIE SAUNDERS! IF YOU'RE SO TIRED, YOU SHOULD GO TO BED EARLIER.

EH? OH, ER — SORRY, MISS.

I CAN'T KEEP THIS UP MUCH LONGER. I'M TELLING CYNTHIA I'M PACKING IT IN.

But, at home —

HAVEN'T YOU NOTICED HOW MUCH BETTER MUM'S BEEN LOOKING SINCE WE'VE HAD EXTRA MONEY COMING INTO THE HOUSE? STILL — IF YOU WANT TO DESTROY HER HAPPINESS . . .

OKAY, I'LL KEEP DOING IT, *IF* YOU HELP OUT BY DOING MY SHARE OF THE HOUSEWORK. IT WOULD GIVE ME MORE TIME TO COPE WITH SCHOOL STUDIES *AND* YOUR DESIGNING.

But then, a month later —

OH, NO! THE FASHION COMPANY IS TAKING A STAND AT THE INTERNATIONAL DESIGNERS EXHIBITION, TO PROMOTE THEIR NEW TEENAGE RANGE — AND *I'M* TO BE THERE.

WHAT'S SO BAD ABOUT THAT? SOUNDS LIKE FUN.

MEMBERS OF THE PUBLIC WILL BE INVITED ONTO THE STAND, SO I CAN DESIGN SPECIAL OUTFITS FOR THEM! BUT I CAN'T EVEN DRAW!

OH WELL, YOU PROMISED YOU'D RESIGN LATER — YOU'D BETTER MAKE IT *SOONER*, BEFORE YOU'RE FIRED!

YOU CAN'T BE SERIOUS! I'D PROBABLY BE OUT OF WORK FOR MONTHS AND THAT WOULD GIVE MUM EVEN MORE TO WORRY ABOUT. YOU COME TO THE EXHIBITION WITH ME, AND WE'LL TRY TO WORK SOMETHING OUT!

And so —

Dell-Dina Designs Just for You

THIS IS MAD! I SKIPPED SCHOOL FOR TODAY, BUT THE EXHIBITION IS ON FOR A WEEK. I DAREN'T MISS ANY MORE LESSONS.

SELF, SELF! THAT'S ALL YOU THINK ABOUT. JUST SHUT UP AND LISTEN. I SEE A WAY OUT OF OUR DIFFICULTIES.

YOU HIDE BEHIND HERE AND DO THE DESIGNS, THEN SMUGGLE THEM OUT TO ME. I CAN PRETEND I'VE JUST DONE THEM.

CYNTHIA, IT WILL *NEVER* WORK . . .

No Boys Allowed!

CONTINUED FROM PAGE 53

SAMMI PALMER'S parents wouldn't let her have boyfriends, so she was dating Graham Rogers behind their backs. But now her little sister, Carly, had seen them together!

WHAT AM I GOING TO DO? I NEVER DREAMT CARLY WOULD BE HERE!

WAIT A MINUTE! *OUR* SCHOOL'S BEEN GIVEN THE DAY OFF 'COS THE HEATING'S BROKEN, BUT CARLY'S AT THE JUNIORS! SHE SHOULD STILL BE IN SCHOOL!

WHAT ARE YOU UP TO, CARLY?

P-PLAYING TRUANT. I DON'T LIKE OUR FIRST LESSON, SO I'M GOING TO PRETEND I WAS AT THE DENTIST. DON'T TELL MUM AND DAD!

OKAY, I WON'T — AS LONG AS *YOU* DON'T SAY YOU SAW ME OUT WITH GRAHAM.

I'M TAKING A HUGE RISK EVERY TIME I GO OUT WITH HIM, AND I'M BEGINNING TO THINK IT'S NOT WORTH IT. HE *IS* GOOD LOOKING, BUT HE'S A FOOTBALL BORE!

At the disco —

THERE'S SHANE GRINNING AT ME AGAIN. NOW FOR *HIM*, ALL THE RISKS MIGHT BE WORTHWHILE . . .

Next day —

GUESS WHAT? I'VE CHUCKED GRAHAM!

GOOD FOR YOU! IT'S TOO RISKY DATING A BOY BEHIND YOUR PARENTS' BACKS.

OH, I DIDN'T CHUCK HIM TO PLEASE *THEM!* I DID IT BECAUSE I FANCY SHANE BUCKLEY AND I THINK HE LIKES ME TOO.

OH, NO!

A few days later, Shane asked Sammi out —

ISN'T IT GREAT? WE'RE GOING TO THE CINEMA!

I JUST HOPE YOU KNOW WHAT YOU'RE DOING.

And —

SHANE'S REALLY NICE! HE ISN'T BORING LIKE GRAHAM, AND HE WANTS TO SEE ME AGAIN ON SATURDAY.

74

CONTINUED ON PAGE 97

PERFECT PARTNERS

PAULA PRENTIS shared a pony with her friend, Lisa. One day, at the riding school —

I LIKE SHARING CONKER WITH LISA, BUT I'M GETTING TOO TALL FOR HIM. I DO WISH I HAD A PONY OF MY OWN.

A little later —

THAT'S ELLEN LACEY ON DARK STAR. HE'S A FANTASTIC PONY.

WELL JUMPED, ELLEN, BUT HE'S BLOWING A BIT. YOU'RE OUT-GROWING HIM.

THEN WE SHOULD START TO LOOK FOR A BUYER FOR STAR.

That evening —

OUR BUSINESS IS DOING WELL AND WE CAN TREAT OURSELVES TO A FEW THINGS — LIKE A NEW CAR. HOW ABOUT YOU, PAULA?

I KNOW WHAT PAULA WANTS — A PONY. SHE SPENDS HOURS AT THE STABLES.

A PONY? FANTASTIC! I KNOW OF A REALLY GOOD PONY FOR SALE — ELLEN LACEY'S DARK STAR.

Dark Star was everything that Paula had dreamed of —

HE MOVES NICELY AND HE'S VERY WELL MANNERED.

OH, STAR — YOU'RE WONDERFUL. YOU DO EXACTLY WHAT I ASK.

F

Paula was right —

AND I'M AFRAID WE WON'T BE ABLE TO AFFORD STAR, PAULA. HIS UPKEEP IS EXPENSIVE AND WE REALLY NEED THE CAPITAL THAT WE'D GET SELLING HIM.

SELL STAR? OHH . . .

HOW WILL I BEAR TO LOSE HIM? BUT I CAN'T MAKE A FUSS. I KNOW HOW UPSET DAD AND MUM ARE.

And so, a few days later —

COME ON, STAR.

I KNOW HOW SAD YOU MUST BE TO SEE HIM GO, PAULA, BUT I PROMISE I'LL TAKE GREAT CARE OF HIM.

I — I KNOW YOU WILL.

STAR WON ALL THOSE FOR ME, AND WE HAD SUCH FUN. I NEED SOMETHING TO TAKE MY MIND OFF THINGS — BUT WHAT?

MRS CHANDLER, WHO ORGANISES THE PONY CLUB TEAMS, RUNS A RIDING SCHOOL. I WONDER IF SHE'D LET ME WORK THERE FOR A BIT?

And so, a little later —

YES, PAULA, I COULD USE SOME HELP HERE — IF YOU DON'T MIND MUCKING OUT AND GROOMING. I CAN OFFER YOU SOME POCKET MONEY IN RETURN.

THANK YOU, MRS CHANDLER!

Paula started work —

THIS ISN'T LIKE HAVING MY OWN PONY, BUT AT LEAST I'M AROUND THEM AGAIN.

Panel 1 (caption: And so, Sasha became Paula's special responsibility —)

YOU'RE ENJOYING THAT, AREN'T YOU, SASHA?

MRS CHANDLER DOESN'T WANT TO TURN HIM OUT IN THE FIELD YET, BECAUSE SHE'S AFRAID HE'LL BE TOO NERVOUS TO BE CAUGHT.

Panel 2 (caption: Paula spent a lot of time working with Sasha —)

SASHA'S REALLY IMPROVED. WOULD YOU LIKE TO TRY RIDING HIM THIS AFTERNOON, WHEN IT'S QUIET?

OH, YES, I WOULD.

Panel 3 (caption: And so, that afternoon —)

IT'S ALL RIGHT, SASHA. I'M NOT GOING TO HURT YOU.

Panel 4

HE'S QUITE DIFFERENT TO STAR. STAR KNEW EVERYTHING. SASHA'S WILLING, BUT IT'S UP TO ME TO HELP TEACH HIM.

GOOD. AFTER A FEW DAYS I'LL TRY HIM WITH ONE OF OUR GOOD RIDERS. IF I'M GOING TO KEEP HIM HE MUST BE USEFUL IN THE RIDING SCHOOL.

Panel 5 (caption: But Sasha was not a success with a school pupil —)

STEADY, BOY!

I THINK PERHAPS YOU'D BETTER RIDE SOMETHING ELSE, NIKKI. PAULA, WILL YOU RIDE SASHA QUIETLY YOURSELF?

Panel 6 (caption: And, a few minutes later —)

OH, SASHA, IF YOU'RE NO USE IN THE RIDING SCHOOL, MRS CHANDLER WILL SELL YOU, AND YOU MIGHT GET ANOTHER BAD HOME.

LISA'S DIARY

MONDAY

Ho! Ho! Ho! Christmas is coming! I hope none of the weedy boys in our year try to trap me under the mistletoe at the Christmas disco. Yuk! Jackie, Debbie and Becky came round and we had a go at making our own Crimbo cards. What a disaster! They looked like something a playschool kid had made! So much for our artistic talents! Gave Martin a telling-off for using my hair mousse. He's such a poser, my little brother.

WEDNESDAY

Went Christmas shopping after school and nearly got crushed to death by the millions of people in the shopping centre. So much for the season of goodwill. Decided to buy Martin his own hair mousse, comb, etc. Save him nicking off with mine all the time! Mum's getting all our favourites in for the festive season. Yummy — the fridge is bulging with tasties! I'll have to do some exercises to get back in shape after Christmas, but who cares? I'm having a fashion crisis about what to wear for the school disco on Friday. Had a look in Ali's wardrobe but her stuff's a bit weird.

FRIDAY

The disco was ace! Well, the sound system only packed up twice — but nothing could spoil our good moods! My mate, David, and I spent the afternoon putting loads of deccies up in the hall and everyone said it looked great. Saw some teachers having a dance. They looked really weird. I must remember not to try and dance when *I* get that old! Too tired to write any more. I'm off to bed for some big ZZZZs!

SATURDAY

Gran phoned to say there's more Christmas pud on the way. Can our stomachs take the pace? Mum and Dad are off to a party tonight. It was nice seeing them all dressed up. Ali, me and Martin played board games all night and cheated at everything. Us Codds are so honourable! (Not!)

TUESDAY

Went round to Gran's for a pre-Christmas tea. She insisted we all try her trial Christmas pud! Let's just say that if we were boats we'd be sunk! Even the dogs tried some and looked like they'd put on a few pounds by the time we went home. Gave Gran one of my home-made cards. She looked pleased but thought my white reindeer was a snowman. Huh! Since when did snowmen have antlers?

THURSDAY

Aargh! The dogs found their Christmas stockings under the tree and proceeded to rip them open and eat all the treats! No tea for them tonight. Got loads of cards from my mates at school. Hope I get some cash from the family so I can take advantage of the January sales! Went round some charity shops and found a nice tablecloth for Gran, some wooden beads for Ali, lovely old picture frames for Mum and a beer tankard Dad will love! Great pressies and helping charities too!

SUNDAY

Hmm — I wonder what's up with Mum and Dad? They didn't look too well this morning. Dad said something about too much punch! They must have come home from the party really late 'cos I didn't even hear their taxi.
Well, it's the big day tomorrow. Couldn't resist a peek downstairs at all the pressies under the tree — now I'm so excited I can't sleep! Happy Christmas, everyone!

89

No Time For Tracy

TRACY MILTON was a pupil at Manorworth Girls' Boarding School. One morning —

WHAT A FAB DAY! JUST WHAT I WANTED FOR THE START OF THE SUMMER HOLIDAYS. DAD'S COMING TO COLLECT ME THIS AFTERNOON. I CAN'T WAIT TO GET HOME AND SEE MUM AND ALL MY FRIENDS!

IT'S VERY QUIET! WHERE *IS* EVERYONE?

STRANGE — ALL THE LUGGAGE HAS GONE. I DIDN'T HEAR ANYONE COME TO TAKE IT AWAY.

AND ALL MY STUFF HAS GONE, TOO! HUH! KERRY AND SHARON AND THE GANG DIDN'T BOTHER TO WAKE ME UP. THEY COULD HAVE WAITED FOR ME!

I HATE IT WHEN THE DORM'S EMPTY LIKE THIS WITHOUT ANY PHOTOS OR PICTURES. I'LL BE GLAD TO GET AWAY!

91

94

95

No Boys Allowed!

CONTINUED FROM PAGE 75

TEA 50p
COFFEE 60p
COLA 70p
ORANGE ...70p
M... 7...

HERE'S A CAKE FOR YOU, HELEN.

THANKS!

WHY DID SAMMI'S MUM HAVE TO BRING ME TO THE CAFE WHERE SAMMI AND SHANE ARE? SHE'S BOUND TO SEE THEM!

SAMMI PALMER'S parents wouldn't let her have boyfriends, so she'd been going out with Graham, and now Shane, behind their backs. Her best friend, Helen, had been covering for her, but now it seemed that Sammi's secret was out.

SHANE'S TAKEN THEIR DRINKS ROUND THE CORNER. SAMMI MUST BE ROUND THERE WAITING FOR HIM, THANK GOODNESS! HER MUM *WON'T* SEE HER SO HER SECRET'S STILL SAFE, BUT IT WAS A CLOSE SHAVE. I'M GOING TO HAVE TO TALK TO HER ABOUT THIS.

Later, at Sammi's house —

WHERE ARE YOU OFF TO TONIGHT?

OH, JUST ROUND TO HELEN'S, MUM.

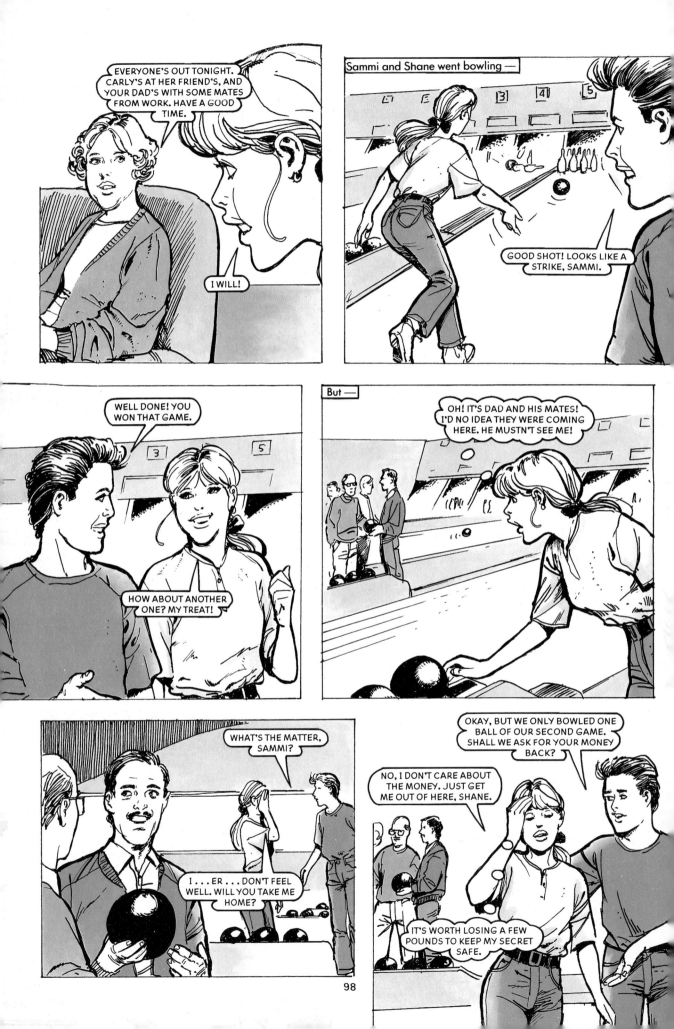

98

99

100

Tinsel Tease

SCRAMBLE!

Which Bunty characters do these stockings belong to? Unscramble the letters in each stocking to find out.

AARLU

RYMA

ILAS

YGSBU

TNUYB

How many of the following words can you find hidden in Santa's sack, reading up, down, backwards, forwards and diagonally?

SANTA'S SACK!

ANNUAL
BUBBLE BATH
CLOTHES
COINS
DOLL
FRUIT
GAME
GLOVES
HAT
JIGSAW
SCARF
SOCKS
SWEETS
TALC
TEDDY
TOY

```
G L O V E S N I O C
Z N P J I G S A W L
A L Q S D A T R O O
T A L C O M V W U T
B U B B L E B A T H
C N F F L X Y S E E
E N R R H Z E K D S
G A A U C A G C D H
I B C I D F T O Y I
K A S T E E W S J K
```

1

2

3

ODD ONE OUT

Which Christmas pudding is the odd one out?

102

STAR TURN!

How many times can you find the word 'STAR' in this wordsearch, reading up, down, backwards, forwards and diagonally?

S	T	A	R	A	T	S	T	A	R
T	S	A	S	T	A	R	R	A	A
A	S	T	A	R	S	R	A	S	T
R	A	A	A	T	A	T	T	S	S
R	A	T	S	R	A	T	S	A	T
A	R	T	A	A	R	S	R	R	A
A	A	A	A	T	A	A	A	R	S
R	T	S	T	A	T	A	T	T	A
A	S	S	R	S	R	R	A	T	S	A
A	A	R	A	T	S	T	A	R	A

GIFT BOX!

Unravel the letters on these gifts to show what's inside, then match them up to the correct label.

V H F A S E R A T E R A

R T L L O

P S P R I E S L

M F U P E R E

DAD

SISTER

GRAN

MUM

COUNTDOWN!

Are there more round baubles than lights on this Christmas tree?

The FOUR MARYS

IT was Saturday, and The Four Marys, Cotter, Simpson, Radleigh and Field, were visiting the nearby town of Elmbury —

ANTIQUES FAIR

INSIDE TOWN HALL ENTRANCE. ADMISSION FREE →

LOOK! AN ANTIQUES FAIR. SHALL WE GO IN?

IT MIGHT BE FUN.

IT'S MY MUM'S BIRTHDAY SOON. MAYBE I'LL FIND A GIFT FOR HER THERE.

THERE ARE QUITE A FEW ST ELMO'S GIRLS HERE. LOOK — MABEL AND VERONICA ARE OVER THERE.

THEN WE'LL GO THE OTHER WAY — BEFORE THOSE TWO SNOBS SEE US.

ANY LUCK, RADDY?

NO. EVERYTHING'S TOO EXPENSIVE AND THE CHEAPER STUFF IS JUST RUBBISH.

LET'S GO BACK TO SCHOOL THEN. WE'LL JUST CATCH THE FOUR-THIRTY BUS.

OH, NO! MABEL AND VERONICA ARE ON IT, AND THE ONLY SPARE SEATS ARE BY THEM.

OLD PHOTOGRAPHS! THEY'RE PICTURES OF TWO ST ELMO'S OLD GIRLS. PERHAPS ONE OF THEM IS THE GIRL'S MOTHER.

Raddy took the locket to the common room —

I FOUND THIS ON THE LIBRARY FLOOR. I THINK A NEW GIRL DROPPED IT.

YOU'D BETTER GIVE IT TO MRS MITCHELL.

Just then —

IS THAT WHAT YOU'VE BOUGHT FOR YOUR MOTHER'S BIRTHDAY? UGH! IT'S CHEAP AND NASTY. DID YOU FIND IT IN A CHRISTMAS CRACKER?

RADDY DIDN'T . . .

LEAVE IT, COTTY. LET THEM THINK WHAT THEY LIKE. I DON'T CARE. I'LL TAKE THE LOCKET TO MRS MITCHELL.

That night —

THAT'S THE FIRE ALARM!

RING! RING!

DON'T PANIC. LEAVE THE BUILDING IN AN ORDERLY MANNER.

WHERE'S THE FIRE?

I CAN'T SEE ANY FLAMES, COTTY.

HERE'S THE FIRE BRIGADE.

107

Half an hour later —

I'M SORRY, EVERYONE. IT WAS A FALSE ALARM. THE FIREMEN HAVE DONE A THOROUGH CHECK OF THE BUILDING AND THERE'S NO SIGN OF A FIRE ANYWHERE.

UNLIKE FIFTY YEARS AGO.

WHAT DOES MISS CREEF MEAN?

TODAY IS THE FIFTIETH ANNIVERSARY OF A BAD FIRE AT ST ELMO'S WHICH CLAIMED THE LIFE OF A PUPIL.

HOW AWFUL!

SPOOKY, I CALL IT.

FIFTY YEARS TO THE DAY AFTER THERE WAS A FIRE HERE, THE FIRE ALARM GOES OFF.

RADDY'S RIGHT. THAT IS ODD. I'D LIKE TO KNOW MORE ABOUT THE OTHER FIRE.

LET'S DO SOME RESEARCH TOMORROW, SIMPY. THE LIBRARY IS FULL OF OLD ARCHIVES.

So, next day, after tea —

HERE ARE SOME OLD NEWSPAPERS FROM THAT TIME.

WE'LL TAKE THEM BACK TO OUR STUDY TO LOOK AT THEM.

WHAT ARE YOU LOT DOING?

WE'RE GOING TO LOOK THROUGH THESE OLD RECORDS.

FANCY SPENDING THE EVENING WITH YOUR HEADS IN A DUSTY OLD BOOK! YOU FOUR ARE SO BORING! WE'RE GOING TO A DISCO.

I'M WEARING MY NEW EARRINGS. BRILL, EH?

108

ANY LUCK?

NOT SO FAR, FIELDY. WAIT A MINUTE!

HERE'S A NEWSPAPER REPORT OF THE FIRE. THE GIRL WHO DIED WAS CALLED SOPHIE FERNIE. HER BEST FRIEND, ALICE PETRIE, ACTED LIKE A HEROINE IN TRYING TO RESCUE HER, BUT SADLY WAS UNSUCCESSFUL. THERE ARE PICTURES OF THEM. LOOK.

THAT'S THE TWO GIRLS IN THE LOCKET!

FIRE AT St ELMO'S

YOU'RE RIGHT, RADDY!

THIS IS SOPHIE FERNIE — THE GIRL WHO DIED.

E AT St ELMO'S

SHE CAN'T HAVE BEEN THE NEW GIRL'S MOTHER THEN. MAYBE IT WAS HER AUNT, OR GREAT-AUNT. THERE'S CERTAINLY A FAMILY RESEMBLANCE.

Next day —

MRS MITCHELL HAS ASKED EVERYONE, AND NOBODY ADMITS TO LOSING A SILVER LOCKET. YOU FOUND IT, SO IT'S UP TO YOU WHAT YOU WANT TO DO WITH IT.

THANK YOU, MISS CREEF.

ONE OF THE PEOPLE PICTURED IN IT IS ALICE PETRIE. MAYBE WE COULD TRACK HER DOWN AND GIVE IT TO HER?

GOOD IDEA, RADDY. SHE'D BE ABOUT SIXTY-TWO NOW, SO CHANCES ARE, SHE'S STILL ALIVE. LET'S ASK MRS MITCHELL IF SHE KNOWS WHERE ALICE PETRIE CAME FROM.

109

And so —

MRS ALICE BOWMAN?

YES.

WE'RE PUPILS AT ST ELMO'S. WE'VE GOT SOMETHING FOR YOU.

MY LOCKET! WHERE DID YOU FIND IT?

IN THE SCHOOL LIBRARY.

THAT'S WHERE I LEFT IT — FIFTY YEARS AGO. I LOVED THAT LOCKET. WHEN A FIRE BROKE OUT IN THE SCHOOL, I STUPIDLY RUSHED BACK INTO THE BURNING BUILDING TO LOOK FOR IT.

AND THAT'S WHEN YOU TRIED TO RESCUE SOPHIE?

NO, EVERYONE THOUGHT *I* WAS A HEROINE THAT DAY — BUT I WASN'T. I WAS JUST A STUPID GIRL WHO RAN BACK INTO A FIRE. SOPHIE TRIED TO RESCUE *ME* — AND DIED IN THE PROCESS. *SHE* WAS THE HEROINE, NOT ME.

BUT THE PAPER SAID . . .

I KNOW. EVERYONE THOUGHT I'D TRIED TO RESCUE SOPHIE. AND I FELT SO GUILTY FOR VIRTUALLY CAUSING MY BEST FRIEND'S DEATH, I HADN'T THE HEART TO PUT THE RECORD STRAIGHT. I'VE KEPT MY GUILTY SECRET FOR FIFTY YEARS.

IT'S SUCH A RELIEF TO TELL SOMEONE THE TRUTH, AT LAST. HOW STRANGE THAT YOU SHOULD FIND THE LOCKET AFTER ALL THESE YEARS. WAS IT WELL HIDDEN?

NO. IT WAS LYING ON THE LIBRARY FLOOR. I THOUGHT A NEW GIRL HAD DROPPED IT. STRANGELY, SHE LOOKED A BIT LIKE THE PICTURE OF SOPHIE.

HOW DID YOU DISCOVER THAT THE PICTURES WERE OF SOPHIE AND ME?

I SEE. HOW STRANGE. TELL ME, DO YOU KNOW THE NAME OF THE GIRL WHO DROPPED THE LOCKET?

THERE WAS A FALSE FIRE ALARM AT ST ELMO'S. OUR TEACHER TOLD US THAT IT WAS THE FIFTIETH ANNIVERSARY OF THE FIRE. WHEN WE LOOKED IT UP IN THE ARCHIVES WE SAW YOUR PICTURES IN AN OLD NEWSPAPER CUTTING.

NO. I'VE NEVER SEEN HER BEFORE, OR SINCE. HER UNIFORM WAS — SORT OF OLD-FASHIONED.

I DON'T THINK YOU EVER WILL SEE HER AGAIN. I . . . I THINK IT MIGHT HAVE BEEN THE GHOST OF SOPHIE.

I CAN'T THINK OF ANOTHER EXPLANATION. PERHAPS SHE WAS TRYING TO TELL ME SHE FORGIVES ME, BY RETURNING MY LOCKET AT LAST.

A GHOST!

I SUPPOSE THAT MUST BE IT. WOW!

A few weeks later —

IT WAS A NICE IDEA OF MRS BOWMAN'S TO DEDICATE A PLAQUE TO SOPHIE'S MEMORY.

IN MEMORY OF SOPHIE FERNIE.

THAT'S IT! I'LL BUY MUM A FRAMED PHOTOGRAPH OF THE CEREMONY FOR HER BIRTHDAY PRESENT. SHE LOVES MEMENTOES OF HER OLD SCHOOL.

A GREAT IDEA! BETTER THAN CHEAP JEWELLERY — EH, MABEL?

HA! HA!

YES. AND MRS MITCHELL ASKED A PHOTOGRAPHER TO COME AND RECORD THE EVENT.

THE END

112

The COMP

ONE November's day, twins Hayley and Becky Sinden were out shopping in Redvale with their mate, Laura Brady —

HEY, LOOK! THE SHOPS HAVE GOT THEIR DECORATIONS UP! IT'LL SOON BE CHRISTMAS!

NOT *THAT* SOON, HAYLEY! WE'VE ONLY *JUST* HAD HALF TERM!

MY SIS STARTS THINKING OF CHRISTMAS AS SOON AS THE SUMMER HOLS ARE OVER, LAURA!

I DO NOT!

YOU DO, TOO! YOU START WRITING OUT YOUR PRESSIE LIST!

I'M OFF, BEFORE YOU START FIGHTING OVER IT! SEE YOU TWO TOMORROW!

At the twins' —

GIRLS! GOOD NEWS — KYLIE'S COMING TO STAY!

WHO? OH! YOU MEAN OUR COUSIN FROM AUSTRALIA!

BUT WE'VE NEVER MET HER, MUM!

WELL, YOU WILL NOW. SHE'S COMING JUST BEFORE CHRISTMAS, AND SHE'LL SPEND IT HERE WITH US!

WOW! IT'LL BE BRILLIANT TO MEET HER! ARE UNCLE RAY AND AUNTIE NOLEEN COMING TOO?

113

NO, THEY CAN'T AFFORD TO ALL COME, BUT YOUR UNCLE WANTS KYLIE TO MEET HER RELATIONS BEFORE SHE'S ANY OLDER.

On Monday morning, at Redvale Comp —

HOW EXCITING! IMAGINE — A COUSIN YOU'VE NEVER MET!

BET SHE'LL FIND A COLD CHRISTMAS WEIRD.

WHAT DO YOU MEAN, CLAIRE?

WELL, DECEMBER IS MIDSUMMER IN OZ, ISN'T IT? WE KNOW THAT FROM THE SOAPS. THEY HAVE CHRISTMAS DINNER ON THE BEACH AND STUFF, DON'T THEY?

OH, WE HADN'T THOUGHT OF THAT!

In assembly —

THERE IS TO BE A SCHOOLS COMPETITION IN THIS AREA — TO DESIGN A CHRISTMAS CARD. THE PRIZE IS A COMPUTER. ANY PUPIL MAY ENTER.

WOW! A COMPUTER!

I CAN'T DRAW FOR TOFFEE, BUT YOU STAND A GOOD CHANCE, LAURA. YOU'RE ALWAYS TOP IN ART. YOU'RE GOOD, TOO, KIKO.

OKAY, LET'S GIVE IT A GO! WHAT HAVE WE GOT TO LOSE?

I'M GOING IN FOR THAT!

ME TOO, HODGE! THINK OF THE COMPUTER GAMES WE COULD GET!

I GUESS DESIGNING AN ORDINARY OLD CHRISTMAS CARD CAN'T BE TOO HARD!

114

So —

DID I SAY IT CAN'T BE HARD? I DON'T HAVE AN IDEA IN MY HEAD! SNOW SCENES, ROBINS, SANTA CLAUS — THEY'VE ALL BEEN DONE!

A CHRISTMAS TREE — NO, THAT'S A BIT BORING. I NEED SOMETHING A BIT MORE EXCITING!

Next day —

FREDDY AND ME HAVE DONE A JOKE CARD. WHEN IT WINS, WE'LL SHARE THE COMPUTER!

SANTA STUCK IN A CHIMNEY. YEAH, HYSTERICAL, HODGE!

I HAVE DRAWN A CHRISTMAS TREE IN A TRADITIONAL JAPANESE GARDEN.

IT'S BEAUTIFUL, KIKO.

STUPID BRAT! WHAT'S A CRUMMY JAPANESE GARDEN GOT TO DO WITH CHRISTMAS?

YOU LOT NEEDN'T THINK YOU'RE GOING TO WIN THAT COMPUTER. NOT WITH THOSE PATHETIC SCRIBBLES, EH, MORAG?

YEAH, PIPPA'S AS GOOD AS WON ALREADY. SHOW 'EM, PIPPA!

A PLAIN CHRISTMAS TREE? WHO DREW IT FOR YOU — YOUR THREE-YEAR-OLD BROTHER?

I DON'T THINK PIPPA STANDS A CHANCE WITH THIS ONE!

A week before Christmas —

HELLO, KYLIE! IT'S LOVELY TO HAVE YOU HERE.

GOSH, SHE'S PRETTY! WHAT A LOVELY TAN SHE'S GOT!

115

YOU'RE BECKY AND YOU'RE HAYLEY, RIGHT? I KNOW YOU FROM PHOTOS!

YEAH, SHE'S THE FUNNY LOOKING ONE.

AND SHE'S JUST FUNNY — IN THE HEAD, THAT IS!

YOU WON'T MIND GOING TO SCHOOL WITH THE GIRLS, WILL YOU? I'VE CLEARED IT WITH THE HEAD. ONLY, YOUR UNCLE MIKE AND I ARE BOTH AT WORK AND YOU'D BE AT A LOOSE END ALL DAY.

NO PROBS, AUNTIE MARY — THAT SOUNDS COOL!

SO WHAT'S THIS PLACE LIKE?

OH, SOME OF THE TEACHERS ARE ALMOST HUMAN . . .

AND WE HAVE LOADS OF TRADITIONS. LIKE ANYONE FROM AUSTRALIA HAS TO DO ALL THE MATHS HOMEWORK FOR EVERYONE ELSE!

HEY, WHOA! I THINK I'LL STAY AT HOME AND PLAY WITH BEN AND TOM!

KYLIE'S REALLY NICE. I LIKE HER, BECKY.

I THINK HODGE AND FREDDY LIKE HER TOO, LAURA. THEY HAVEN'T TAKEN THEIR EYES OFF HER SINCE SHE CAME IN!

KYLIE, PERHAPS YOU COULD GIVE US A LITTLE TALK IN OUR NEXT GEOGRAPHY PERIOD — TELL US A BIT ABOUT WHAT CHRISTMAS IS LIKE DOWN UNDER!

NO WORRIES!

ME NEXT, KYLIE!

NO, ME!

HMPH! CAN'T THINK WHAT THEY ALL SEE IN HER. THAT AWFUL, COMMON AUSSIE ACCENT!

POOR JAYNE! *SHE'S* USED TO BEING THE CENTRE OF ATTENTION!

Just then, Sooty Cole took the mike —

THE FIRST PRIZE WINNER IN THE CHRISTMAS CARD DESIGN COMPETITION IS A REDVALE PUPIL. STEP FORWARD — PIPPA CRAGSTON!

WHAT?

THAT KIDDIE DRAWING OF HERS WON?

SHE GOT THE COMPUTER. SHE'LL BE GLOATING OVER US FOREVER!

HERE'S YOUR CERTIFICATE, PIPPA.

WHERE'S MY COMPUTER?

YOU DON'T GET THE COMPUTER PERSONALLY, PIPPA. THE COMPUTER GOES TO THE WINNER'S *SCHOOL.*

HUH! IF I'D KNOWN THAT, I WOULDN'T HAVE ENTERED THE CRUMMY CONTEST!

On the last day of term —

BACK HOME, WE CELEBRATE CHRISTMAS DAY WITH A BARBIE ON THE BEACH. AND ON CHRISTMAS EVE, OUR TOWN HOLDS A SURFING COMP, AND IT'S REAL HOT AND SUNNY . . .

I'M SORRY YOU DIDN'T WIN, LAURA. I THOUGHT YOUR COLLAGE DESIGN WAS WAY THE BEST.

I'M NOT WORRIED, BECKY. PIPPA PRODUCED THE SORT OF DESIGN THE JUDGES WANTED. AND WASN'T HER FACE A PICTURE WHEN SHE FOUND OUT ABOUT THE COMPUTER?

YOUR TALK IN GEOGRAPHY WAS A BIG HIT, KYLIE. EVERYONE ENJOYED IT.

WHAT? OH, THANKS, ROZ.

Next day —

WANT TO GO CHRISTMAS SHOPPING, KYLIE? WE'LL SHOW YOU THE HIGH SPOTS OF REDVALE. KYLIE? YOU OKAY?

HUH? ER — YES. I'M FINE.

SOMETHING'S UP WITH KYLIE, BECKY.

I THINK *I* KNOW WHAT'S WRONG, HAYLEY.

KYLIE, YOU'RE FEELING HOMESICK, AREN'T YOU?

SORRY, BUT YES, I AM. IT'S JUST — IT'S SO COLD HERE. I CAN'T HELP THINKING WHAT THEY'LL ALL BE DOING BACK HOME.

On Christmas Eve —

IT'S NOT THAT I DON'T LIKE BEING HERE WITH YOU. DON'T THINK THAT —

WE DON'T, SILLY!

HMM, I THINK I'M GETTING AN IDEA.

KYLIE'S JUST COMING. DON'T FORGET, KEEP HER OUT AT LEAST TWO HOURS! THAT'LL GIVE US TIME.

WE WILL, BECKY. WE'VE TOLD HER WE NEED HER HELP TO CHOOSE PRESSIES FOR YOU TWO. WE'LL SEE YOU AT LUNCHTIME!

119

LUCKY YOU!
Colour — Indigo
Number — 7
Jewel — Opal
Day — Saturday

LIBRA
(24 September-23 October)
Sign — scales
Ruling planet — Venus

BEST FRIENDS
Librans get on like a house on fire with Taureans, Geminis, Leos, other Librans, Aquarians and Pisceans. In fact, Librans are so easy-going they get on with most people.

GOOD BITS
(Yippee!)
Easy-going, romantic, artistic and peaceful.

BAD BITS
(Boo!)
Indecisive, lazy and too talkative!

SPECIAL DAY IN 1996
August 23

FAMOUS LIBRANS
Anneka Rice — October 4
Caron Keating — October 5
Dawn French — October 11
Cliff Richard — October 14
Dannii McMahon — October 20

JUST THE JOB
Beautician, dress designer, hairdresser, artist, receptionist or juggler!

JUST THE JOB
Mathematician, politician, farmer, architect, dentist, civil servant or a musician.

LUCKY YOU!
Colour — Green
Number — 3
Jewel — Garnet
Day — Tuesday

BEST FRIENDS
Capricorns are usually drawn to Virgoans, Scorpians and Taureans.

FAMOUS CAPRICORNS
Annie Lennox — December 25
Rowan Atkinson — January 6
Rod Stewart — January 10
Stephen Hendry — January 13
Kevin Costner — January 18

SCORPIO
(24 October-22 November)
Sign — scorpion
Ruling planet — Pluto

FAMOUS SCORPIANS
Julia Roberts — October 28
Winona Ryder — October 29
Prince Charles — November 14
Boris Becker — November 22

BAD BITS
(Boo!)
Jealous, obstinate, secretive, overly competitive and suspicious.

GOOD BITS
(Yippee!)
Energetic, imaginative, determined, sincere, intelligent and sporty.

JUST THE JOB
Psychiatrist, police work, insurance agent, butcher or anything to do with the Forces.

LUCKY YOU!
Colour — Dark red
Number — 4
Jewel — Topaz
Day — Wednesday

SPECIAL DAY IN 1996
February 11

BEST FRIENDS
Scorpians are usually chummy with Cancerians, Capricorns and Pisceans.

SAGITTARIUS
(23 November-22 December)
Sign — the archer
Ruling planet — Jupiter

JUST THE JOB
Teacher, lawyer, vet, explorer, sports personality, writer or a jockey!

LUCKY YOU!
Colour — Pale blue
Number — 2
Jewel — Turquoise
Day — Friday

FAMOUS SAGITTARIANS
Tina Turner — November 26
Gary Lineker — November 30
Brad Pitt — December 18
Noel Edmonds — December 22

GOOD BITS
(Yippee!)
Happy go-lucky, truthful, fun-loving, open-minded, optimistic and athletic.

BAD BITS
(Boo!)
Tactless, careless, irresponsible, impatient and changeable.

SPECIAL DAY IN 1996
August 23

BEST FRIENDS
Friendships will usually be found amongst Arians, Taureans, Leos and other Sagittarians.